JOSEPH AND THE AMAZING TECHNICOLOR DREAMCOAT

words by
TIM RICE

music by
ANDREW LLOYD WEBBER

THE REALLY USEFUL GROUP Ltd.
LONDON
Order No: RUG 37234

NOTE

The history of *Joseph* is a curious one, inasmuch as it has developed from a twenty-minute cantata for schools into a full-length musical.

The material in this score will, we hope, stand up to a concert performance without staging. The score can be used as the basis from which the music can be interpreted freely.

ANDREW LLOYD WEBBER and TIM RICE

'Joseph' logo cover design © Copyright 1991 RUG Ltd.

Original edition published (1975) by Novello & Co. Ltd.
This edition © Copyright 1991 The Really Useful Group Ltd., London.

DURATION ABOUT ONE HOUR

® Technicolor is the registered trademark of the Technicolor Group of Companies.

CONTENTS

ACT ONE

ACT TWO

'Choir' refers to children's voices, 'Chorus' to adults.

ORCHESTRATION

Flute, doubling Piccolo and Clarinet in B flat
Clarinet in B flat, doubling Soprano Saxophone in B flat and Bass Clarinet

Trumpet in B flat
Trombone, doubling Tuba

Guitar
Bass Guitar

Piano, doubling Harpsichord and Organ

Drums
Percussion:
  Xylophone
  Triangle
  Conga
  Bongos
  Glockenspiel
  Tambourine
  Guiro
  Chinese Blocks
  Stones
  Hooves

Conductor's Score, Instrumental parts as above & children's choir parts are all available on hire only.

JOSEPH AND THE AMAZING TECHNICOLOR DREAMCOAT

Words by
TIM RICE

ACT ONE

Music by
ANDREW LLOYD WEBBER

1 JACOB and SONS/JOSEPH'S COAT

Joseph and the amazing technicolor dreamcoat

4

*The voice-parts for the Brothers are optional from ⬜C to ⬜G.

Joseph and the amazing technicolor dreamcoat

Joseph and the amazing technicolor dreamcoat

6

Joseph and the amazing technicolor dreamcoat

Joseph and the amazing technicolor dreamcoat

8

Joseph and the amazing technicolor dreamcoat

Joseph and the amazing technicolor dreamcoat

10

Joseph and the amazing technicolor dreamcoat

Joseph and the amazing technicolor dreamcoat

12

Joseph and the amazing technicolor dreamcoat

Joseph and the amazing technicolor dreamcoat

Joseph and the amazing technicolor dreamcoat

Joseph and the amazing technicolor dreamcoat

Joseph and the amazing technicolor dreamcoat

2 JOSEPH'S DREAMS

Relaxed ♩. = 66

A NARRATOR

Jo - seph's coat an - noyed his bro - thers, But what makes us mad Are the

BROTHERS

things that Jo - seph tells us of the dreams he's of - ten had. I

JOSEPH

B

dreamed that in the fields one day, at corn - col - lect - ing time,____

Joseph and the amazing technicolor dreamcoat

Your e – le – ven sheaves of corn all turned and bowed to mine, My

C

sheaf was quite a sight to see, a gold – den sheaf and tall.

Yours were green and se – cond-rate, and real – ly ra – ther small.

D

BROTHERS

This is not the

Joseph and the amazing technicolor dreamcoat

Joseph and the amazing technicolor dreamcoat

BROTHERS on - ly is he tact - less but he's al - so ra - ther dim,___ For there's e - le - ven of us___ and there's on - ly one of him.___ The dreams of course will not come true, That is we think they won't come true, That

Joseph and the amazing technicolor dreamcoat

24

Joseph and the amazing technicolor dreamcoat

3 POOR, POOR JOSEPH

Fast ♩ = 160

half tempo ♩ = 80

NARRATOR *f*

Next day, far from home, the bro-thers planned the re-pul - sive crime.

BROTHERS

Let us grab him now, do him in while we've got the time.

NARRATOR

This they did and made the most of it,

Tore his coat and flung him in a pit.

B BROTHERS

Let us leave him here all a - lone, and he's bound to die.

NARRATOR

When some Ish - mael - ites, a hair - y crew, came rid - ing by.

Repeat these four bars if required

Joseph and the amazing technicolor dreamcoat

C
In a flash the bro-thers changed their plan.

BROTHERS
SOLO (spoken) ALL
We need cash, let's sell him if we can.

NARRATOR & CHOIR
Poor, poor Jo - seph, what-'cha gon - na do? Things look bad for you, hey, what-'cha gon - na do?

D
BROTHERS
Could you use a slave, you hair-y bunch of Ish-mael-ites? Young, strong, well-be-haved,

Joseph and the amazing technicolor dreamcoat

Joseph and the amazing technicolor dreamcoat

4 ONE MORE ANGEL IN HEAVEN

The vocal arrangement included here may require to be modified to suit the available resources. For reference, a melody cue will be found on a separate line.

Joseph and the amazing technicolor dreamcoat

know you had a ___ do - zen sons, well now that's ___ not quite true,-

Oo, ___
But feel no sor - row, do ___ not grieve— he
Oo, ___ do ___ not grieve—
Oo, ___

would not want you ___ to. There's one more an - gel in

Joseph and the amazing technicolor dreamcoat

34

Joseph and the amazing technicolor dreamcoat

Joseph and the amazing technicolor dreamcoat

36

Joseph and the amazing technicolor dreamcoat

Joseph and the amazing technicolor dreamcoat

Joseph and the amazing technicolor dreamcoat

40

Joseph and the amazing technicolor dreamcoat

tough but we're gon-na get by.___ There's one less place at our ta-ble,___ There's one more tear in my eye,___ But Jo-seph, the things that you stood for, Like de-mo-cra-cy ne-ver die._____

5 POTIPHAR

Jo - seph was ta - ken to E - gypt in chains and sold,

CHOIR

Ah

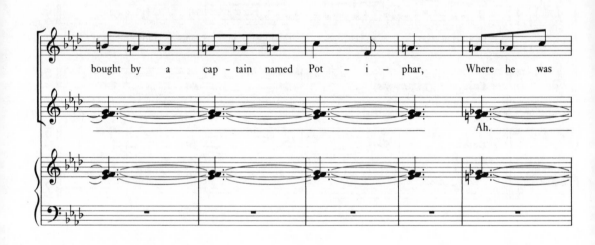

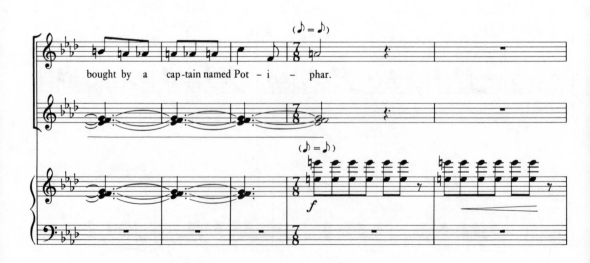

Having made a fortune buying__ shares in py-ra-mids,
It's all there in chap-ter thir-ty-nine of Gen-e-sis.__

Pot-i-phar had made a huge pile,
She was beau-ti-ful but e-vil,

Owned a large per-cen-tage of the__ Nile,
Saw a lot of men a-gainst his__ will,

Meant that he could real-ly
He would have to tell her

Joseph and the amazing technicolor dreamcoat

NARRATOR & CHOIR

live in___ style and he did.___
that she___ still___ was his.___
Jo - seph was an
Jo - seph's looks and

un - im - por - tant slave who found he liked his mas - ter, Con - se - quen - tly
hand - some fig - ure had at - trac - ted her at - ten - tion, Ev - 'ry morn - ing

(NARRATOR & CHOIR)

worked much har - der, ev - en with de - vo - tion. Pot - i - phar could
she would beck - on
Jo - seph want - ed

v. 2 MRS. POTIPHAR

Come and lie with me, love.

Joseph and the amazing technicolor dreamcoat

48

see that Jo - seph was a cut a - bove the av' - rage, Made him lea - der
to re - sist her, till one day she proved too ea - ger. Jo - seph cried in

of his house-hold, max - i - mum pro - mo - tion.

vain

v. 2 JOSEPH

Please stop! I don't be - lieve in free love.

Tempo I

Tempo I

(Cow-bell)

Tempo I

(Cow-bell)

simile

Joseph and the amazing technicolor dreamcoat

50

6 CLOSE EVERY DOOR

Joseph and the amazing technicolor dreamcoat

Joseph and the amazing technicolor dreamcoat

JOSEPH *mp* **K**

Just give me a num - ber in - stead of my name, For - get all a - bout me, and let me de - cay.

Dal S al ⊕ e poi CODA
(JOSEPH & CHOIR) **N** *f*

lone, For we know we shall find our own peace of mind, For we have been prom - ised a land of our own.

rall.

Joseph and the amazing technicolor dreamcoat

7 GO, GO, GO JOSEPH

set._____ Hey Jo - seph! You're not beat - en

B D Tempo di Go-go
+ CHORUS MEN *ad lib.*

yet. Go, go, go Jo - seph, you know what they say._____ Hang on now

Jo - seph, you'll make it some day._____ Sha la la Jo — seph, you're do - ing fine,

Tempo I (NARRATOR)

_____ You and your Dream - coat — a-head of your time._____ The

E NARRATOR
mp

In the pri – son cell with Jo – seph were two ve – ry fright-ened men.___

Gm F Eb D7 Gm

BUTLER & BAKER

We don't think that we will ev – er see the light of day a-gain.___

Gm F Eb D Gm

Hey Jo – seph! Help us if___ you can, We've had dreams that we don't un – der –

Bb F F C G Bb F C F

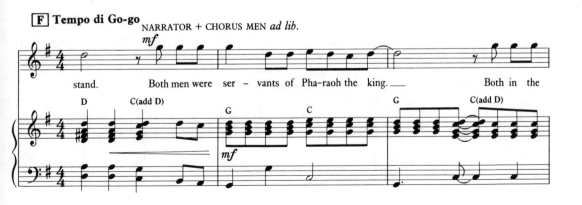

F **Tempo di Go-go** NARRATOR + CHORUS MEN *ad lib.*
mf

stand. Both men were ser – vants of Pha-raoh the king.___ Both in the

D C(add D) G C G C(add D)

mf

Joseph and the amazing technicolor dreamcoat

Joseph and the amazing technicolor dreamcoat

60 L

JOSEPH

mp

Sad to say your dream is not the kind of dream I'd like to get. Phar - aoh has it in for you, your ex - e - cu - tion date is set. Don't re - ly on all I said___ I saw,___ It's just that I have not been wrong___ be -

Joseph and the amazing technicolor dreamcoat

Joseph and the amazing technicolor dreamcoat

Joseph and the amazing technicolor dreamcoat

ACT TWO
8 PHARAOH STORY

64

Joseph and the amazing technicolor dreamcoat

Joseph and the amazing technicolor dreamcoat

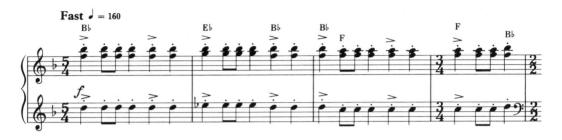

Joseph and the amazing technicolor dreamcoat

68

What to do? What-ev – er could it mean?

A LIVELY LAD

Then some live – ly lad said, I know of a bloke in jail

Who is hot on dreams, could ex – plain old Phar – aoh's tale.

NARRATOR PHARAOH

Phar – aoh said, Fetch this Jo – seph man,

Joseph and the amazing technicolor dreamcoat

Joseph and the amazing technicolor dreamcoat

70

Joseph and the amazing technicolor dreamcoat

seven fat cows came out of the Nile, a - ha,
seven beautiful ears of corn, a - ha,

ha, And
ha, They were

CHORUS Bap shu wa du wa bap bap shu wa du wa,

right behind these fine health - y an - i - mals came
ripe, they were gold - en but you've guessed it, right be - hind them there were

Joseph and the amazing technicolor dreamcoat

Joseph and the amazing technicolor dreamcoat

ha,
did,
But it
But

Bap___ shu wa du wa bap___ bap___ shu wa du wa,

A

A

did – n't make them fat – ter like___ such a mon – ster sup – per
Jo – seph, here's the punch – line, it's___ real – ly gon – na blow your

E

E

should,
mind.
The
The

Bap___ shu wa du wa bap___ bap___ shu wa du wa,

E

E

Joseph and the amazing technicolor dreamcoat

74

thin cows were as thin as they had ev – er, ev – er, ev – er, ev – er
bad corn was as bad as it had ev – er, ev – er, ev – er, ev – er

Ah,

to CODA ⊕

been.
been.

This dream has got me baf-fled, hey, Jo - seph what does it

mean?

Now you know that kings ain't stu – pid, But

Ah

Joseph and the amazing technicolor dreamcoat

Joseph and the amazing technicolor dreamcoat

Joseph and the amazing technicolor dreamcoat

10 PHARAOH'S DREAMS EXPLAINED

Joseph and the amazing technicolor dreamcoat

78

fu - ture does-n't look so bright, E - gypt's luck will change complete-ly ov - er -night And

ba   ba ba   ba   ba ba   ba ba   ba ba,

fa - mine's hand___ will stalk the land__ With food an all - time

oo - ee - oo,___   oo - ee - oo - oo, __   Ba   ba

low.__   No - ble king, there is no doubt   What your dream is all a -

ba,___

Joseph and the amazing technicolor dreamcoat

Joseph and the amazing technicolor dreamcoat

fa - mine With a flair for e - co - no - mic plann-ing. But__ who this man would

ah,

be I just don't know, who this man would

who this man would be I just don't know,

HIGH VOICES

CHORUS who this man would be I just don't, who this man would

LOW VOICES

Joseph and the amazing technicolor dreamcoat

11 STONE THE CROWS

Movendo ♩ = 120

NARRATOR
Phar - aoh said,

PHARAOH
Well stone the crows, this Jo - seph is a cle - ver kid.

Who'd have thought that four - teen cows could mean the things he said they did.

Joseph and the amazing technicolor dreamcoat

84

Joseph and the amazing technicolor dreamcoat

Joseph and the amazing technicolor dreamcoat

Jo - seph saw that food was gath - ered rea - dy for the years a - head.

oo — ee - oo — ee - oo — ee - oo,

Se - ven years of fa - mine fol - lowed, E - gypt did not mind a bit, The

oo — ee - oo — ee - oo — ee - oo,

first re - cord - ed ra - tion - ing in hist' - ry was a hit.

oo — ee - oo — ee - oo — ee - oo,

Joseph and the amazing technicolor dreamcoat

Joseph and the amazing technicolor dreamcoat

Joseph and the amazing technicolor dreamcoat

Joseph and the amazing technicolor dreamcoat

NARRATOR: This could be a hap - py end - ing, per - fect place to stop the show,

JOSEPH: break.

CHOIR: Oo - ee - oo - ee - oo - ee - oo,

Jo - seph af - ter all has got a - bout as far as he can go.

oo - ee - oo - ee - oo - ee - oo,

Joseph and the amazing technicolor dreamcoat

Joseph and the amazing technicolor dreamcoat

12 THOSE CANAAN DAYS★

★It is desirable that, in addition to the orchestra, this number should be accompanied (possibly by one of the Brothers) on the accordion.

cold. / seen.
We strolled down the bou-le-vard to-ge-ther,
It's fun - ny but since we lost Jo - seph,

And ev' - ry-thing round us was___ fine.___
We've gone to the o - ther ex - treme.___

Now the fields are dead and bare, No *joie - de - viv - re* a - ny-where, *Et*
No - one comes to din - ner now, We'd on - ly eat them a - ny-how, I

main - te - nant we drink a bit - ter wine.
ev - en find I'm mis - sing Jo - seph's dreams.
Those Ca - naan days we used to

Joseph and the amazing technicolor dreamcoat

Joseph and the amazing technicolor dreamcoat

13 THE BROTHERS COME
TO EGYPT/GROVEL, GROVEL

Joseph and the amazing technicolor dreamcoat

Joseph and the amazing technicolor dreamcoat

Joseph and the amazing technicolor dreamcoat

Joseph and the amazing technicolor dreamcoat

Joseph and the amazing technicolor dreamcoat

Joseph and the amazing technicolor dreamcoat

quite jus - ti - fied. I shall give you what you came for____ and

cringe, bow, stoop, fall. Wor - ship, wor - ship,

A♭m   D♭11 G♭   D♭7   E♭m   C♭

lots more be - side.

beg, kneel, sponge, Thank you, thank you, cringe, bow, stoop, fall.

A♭m   E♭m   C♭   D♭   E♭m

(BROTHERS)   **Tempo I** ♩ = 132   NARRATOR

Wor - ship, wor - ship, beg, kneel, sponge, crawl. Jo-seph

E♭m   C♭   D♭   E♭   E♭m

hand - ed them sack - loads of food   And they grov - elled with base gra - ti -

G♭   D♭7   D♭7

Joseph and the amazing technicolor dreamcoat

Joseph and the amazing technicolor dreamcoat

14 WHO'S THE THIEF?

Joseph and the amazing technicolor dreamcoat

Joseph and the amazing technicolor dreamcoat

Joseph and the amazing technicolor dreamcoat

Joseph and the amazing technicolor dreamcoat

Joseph and the amazing technicolor dreamcoat

Joseph and the amazing technicolor dreamcoat

15 BENJAMIN CALYPSO

Brightly ♩ = 144

BROTHERS *mf*

Oh no,___ not he,___

How you can ac-cuse him is a my-ste — ry. Save him,___ take me,___

Ben-ja-min is straight-er dan de tall palm tree.___

ONE BROTHER

1 I hear de steel drums sing dere song,___ Dey're sing-in' man you know you
2 Sure as de tide wash de gol-den sand,___ Ben-ja-min is an

Joseph and the amazing technicolor dreamcoat

the following eight bars sung three times

La la la___ la la la la la,

La la la___ la la la la,

La la la___ la la

la la la,___ La la la___ la la la la.

1,2

16 JOSEPH ALL THE TIME

la la. And Jo - seph knew by this his bro - thers now were hon - est

mf NARRATOR

mf sempre

Joseph and the amazing technicolor dreamcoat

Joseph and the amazing technicolor dreamcoat

Joseph and the amazing technicolor dreamcoat

17 JACOB IN EGYPT

18 ANY DREAM WILL DO

Joseph and the amazing technicolor dreamcoat

Joseph and the amazing technicolor dreamcoat

col - ours fa - ded ___ in - to dark - ness, I was left a - lone.

col - ours fa - ded in - to dark - ness, Ah _____ ah _____

col - ours fa - ded in - to dark - ness,

May I re - turn to the be -

May I re - turn

May I re - turn ___

Joseph and the amazing technicolor dreamcoat

Joseph and the amazing technicolor dreamcoat

124

Joseph and the amazing technicolor dreamcoat

Joseph and the amazing technicolor dreamcoat

Printed in Great Britain